Old Age Can Wait!

Agnes Jelhof Jensen

.WARM
.WISE
.WITTY

Acknowledgements

Thank you all.

It was a wonderful experience to write about seniors who refuse old age. A learning process I shall never forget.

May this book help the fearful and give them courage.

Agnes Jelhof Jensen

Cover art by Susanne Højgaard

Typography by Edward Bassett

Printed in Canada
By Edmonton Copy & Printing

ISBN 0-9680870-3-5
First Edition

Published in Canada by Danbooks
7808 Rowland Road
Edmonton, Alberta T6A 3W1

Though old as the hills

If you count my years

My heart still harbours

A youthful laughter

Because I can taste

The sweetness of life

By the same author, in Danish:

Hallo Canada

Midt mellem Le og Græde

Glemmebogen

Dilemma

Huset i Canada

In English

Dilemma

Published by Oberon Press   1995

Hello Canada

Published by Danbooks   1998

Translated by Bodil Jelhof Jensen

No One Must Know

Published by Danbooks   1998

Contents

Chapter 1

ONCE A SENIOR...

That day will for always be engraved in my memory. It was half a year before I – with some luck – would turn 65 when I received the first dire warning of things to come.

The local postman brought a brown envelope to my door, the kind any government will use when it concerns dog tags, or traffic fines or any other form used for collecting hidden taxes, and that same local postman would have placed it very carefully in my mailbox if there had been one. That much you can trust. Once your letters are that close to your abode you will usually receive them.

– You do not have a mailbox, he complained when he discovered me, lurking behind a lilac bush because I always try to avoid confrontations with bus drivers and mail carriers.

No. I advanced slowly and grudgingly. No mailbox.

– Every house should have a mailbox.

Yes.

– How do you expect to get letters, he demanded. He was new in the district.

– Usually people write them and put stamps on the envelope and deposit them in an official mailbox and hope that somebody sooner or later will deliver them to my door – although that is not always the case.

I have faced that situation and that conversation with many a mail carrier over that last 40 years if I did not manage to hide behind the lilac bush…

– How can I deliver your letter? He held up one of the famous brown envelopes and I started wondering where I had been driving during the last two weeks and how fast.

I pointed to my front door and its letter slot. I tried a shade of a smile, very cautiously.

He never noticed but handed me the letter and trotted down the driveway. His back told me that I was not the only obtrusive customer on his route.

The letter I held in my hand was very official with my full name shining through its window, followed by a number. That number business always gets my dander up. Not that I am deliriously enthusiastic about my name. But it is a name. Numbers make me nervous. Any kind of numbers.

My thoughts go back to the night when I was standing in our smoke-filled house on the south side of the North Saskatchewan River in Edmonton, the capital of Alberta – so far – and a young policeman arrived ahead of the fire trucks.

He asked me courteously to spell my name and added:

– How old are you, madam?

– What do you mean? I bellowed. I have been a Girl Guide captain; I know how to bellow.

– I mean how old are you, madam?

At this point the smoke forced us out of the house onto the front lawn where the children's father was on lookout for the fire engines. He took over the rest of the interview. He did not mind telling the police officer that he was 49 and his coughing wife half a year older.

– Is she fifty? the young uniform asked.

The arrival of the fire engines drowned out all other noises. The neighbours descended on our front lawn as neighbours do when they hear or see an ambulance or a police car or a fire engine. The sirens are like magic. Any form of calamity brings misdirected curiosity to the forefront.

– Oh, an accident... Drive slowly, dear. Let us see what is going on. It looks serious... Two ambulances. I wonder how many have been killed...

That night there was only a lot of smoke and no fire.

– Where there is smoke, there is fire, our teacher preached

She did not know our house. The belt in the furnace was stuck and produced the smoke.

– Good night, madam, smiled the police officer. He knew!

I was only fifty then and already hated all numbers. Right now I would love to say that I was only 50 years old.

But the brown envelope with the window disclosed for anybody who could read that I very soon would turn 65, and the content of the letter was that I would become a senior and by Canadian law I was entitled to some benefits.

A senior. The thought was overwhelming, mostly because from now on I would always be a senior. The situation would never change. Not until the day my heart stopped beating, and that was not a very uplifting thought. The very thought made me sad and dejected. I was no longer just an adult. I was a senior citizen. It sounded so serious – as if I was half-dead already, or at least not up to scratch. Full of hidden diseases. Mentally slowing down as old age was creeping closer.

Old age! Dear me! Half a year from now I would be caught in the web. There were already too many senior citizens, the paper told us daily, and this ever-growing multitude of older people was the reason governments went broke. The worst thing was there was nothing a person could do. You could not hope or promise that you would be younger tomorrow. There was no escape. My number was up.

The minister of the crown who had signed the letter congratulated me, as far as I understood it. Ministerial letters are always hard to translate even if you think you know the original language. He was probably 45. He knew nothing about old age.

Anyway, I comprehended that six months from now I would be eligible for old age pension.

Old age pension.

For a fleeting minute I thought that I would rather not. Especially when it dawned on me that the enclosed application, complete with my name and number and exact age should be returned, witnessed by a non-related person who thus would verify that I was about to turn 65 because I was born 65 years ago.

The wheels were turning. My back was stooped and I felt the weight of a bleak future with an open grave at the end. I lifted a deep sigh up against the blue sky which remained blue. Life can be so cruel.

All this happened before the computers took over and although the typewriter had been invented, government letters could gather much dust and age considerably from the time they were received in an office to the day they wandered out to the paying public again, especially if the letter was marked "Reply Soonest".

Nothing has really changed. It can happen today, but now we can blame the computer.

– Sorry, it was down all morning. Yes, that is why the letter is 3 weeks late.

Anyway, if I should have any hope of receiving my old age pension half a year hence, I had better find someone to sign the application today and get the letter off.

But who? Who should that non-related person be?

That was a problem. I had to find a complete stranger, perhaps bribe a bartender in the other end of the city. This was serious business. We were no longer talking about 49 or 50. Old age – senior for life. Words I had never used in connection with myself. It had always been someone else – the older generation, grandmothers, great-grandmothers, distant in-laws I hardly knew. Neighbours and a few acquaintances. Now it was my turn.

I could, of course, trash the letter. Forget about it. Pretend I never received it. But then I would, probably, get another one telling me that I was still approaching 65 but now it was too late to apply for an old age pension. Government offices! Give them a finger and they will take your shaking old hand.

What to do... Oh, what to do!

I thought about the bridge club, and the choir and the knitting bee. I know a few people, and Edmonton is not a deserted island, no matter what they think in the East.

Yes, I thought a lot and settled on a neighbour, a very nice and busy lady. I just had to figure out how to go about it. First I would fold the document so she could not see what she was signing. Then I would catch her on a Wednesday morning when she hurried to her weekly volunteer work. In her rush she would not have time to investigate. The whole street follows Dido's departure each Wednesday morning. She is always late and dashes off in her little red car while mothers and grandmothers and ordinary neighbours gather their children and grandchildren and dogs and cats so nothing will be in her way.

It worked out beautifully. That Wednesday the sun was smiling, the breeze was warm and soft, and Dido came running out of her house in a panic to start her little red car and rush off to her good deed of the week. That morning she seemed to be extra late, rushing like mad.

– The dog threw up in the dining room on the carpet. Wouldn't you know it? She only makes a mess on Wednesday, Dido complained when I approached her and her car with my carefully folded official document.

– She is a very clever dog, she knows it is Wednesday. Dido waved and got into the car and had it started in one soft fluent motion.

– Dido, would you please sign this for me. My hand was steady, my voice was steady, and I brought a pen.

– Sure. What are neighbours for? Dido wrote her signature and handed me back the document without paying much attention. A sigh of relief emerged from my troubled breast up towards the blue Alberta sky. She was easing away from the curb when she leaned out muttered, mostly to herself:

– We all thought you were 65 last year.

Then she disappeared round the corner, pen and all.

The day came – the day when I turned 65. It was not a sunny and bright day to ease the blow. My birthday is in October, at the very end of a long and dreary month, and no matter where in the world I have celebrated it, there has always been heavy grey and wet clouds hanging down over the roofs, hiding the surroundings as if they were ashamed of the event. It seldom rains – as if the weather cannot be bothered to go all the way. It is just a miserable, unpleasant, uncomfortable, almost disgusting day...

I know there are beautiful days in October. It is fall, the leaves are turning, the air smells pleasantly of peace and quiet – a little damp, but that is only nice after a long dry summer. Somebody has a fire going somewhere, the smoke stirs forgotten pleasant memories. It is good to be alive when the October sun dances over a rainbow of colours only nature can paint. But that is not on my birthday. If you wake up one morning in October and discover that everything outside has lost colour and form in a dirty grey fog, and you would rather stay in bed all day because nothing entices you to get up – then you know I am one year older.

This day, this fatal day when I grudgingly joined the ranks of seniors in order to get my old age pension was exactly as wet and damp and grey and dark as all the other birthdays I remember.

I had decided not to celebrate, not making a big to-do out of it. After all, it was not a round birthday, it was a rather unimportant one except for the fact that the government had decided it was vital. I have never allowed any government to influence what is important in my life. Why start now!

The kids were coming for dinner with their families. Strictly a family affair, nothing else. I strolled around in my housecoat during the early grey morning and talked to my dogs as usual when the doorbell interrupted our pleasant one-sided conversation.

Outside was a young man with a huge bouquet of flowers. He inspected me and decided he had seen worse. I think.

The sight of flowers produces a rich warm feeling. It runs from the neck, down the spine, into the legs and it stays there for the longest time. Who would send me flowers on my birthday? Who remembered, and where did I have some change to give this wonderful young man who occupied my doorstep with glad tidings in his arms.

– Lady, he said – could you keep these flowers for your next door neighbour till she returns. I ain't got no time to wait or come back…

A bit of the warm feeling evaporated. But then I did not have to worry about a gratuity. After all, the flowers were not for me.

– It is her birthday, you know. A dirty thumb pointed at the neighbour's house.

– Getting old, the youngster quipped -- turning 50 she is.

I closed the door between us.

All in all it was a great day. Members of the bridge club phoned and pretended I turned 59, and so did the salesman who insisted it was time for me to decide where I wanted to rest.

– In my bed, I suggested.

He laughed politely as salesmen can do.

– I mean your final resting-place, madam. We have some beautiful plots you will enjoy. There are only a few left. The view is absolutely striking.

– How can I enjoy the view when I am dead?

The polite laugh again.

– The thought, the very thought that you one day will stretch your weary legs...

We left it at that although I received a brochure a couple of days later with a picture of the view I could enjoy when I passed away. The thought left me with a feeling that it had not been a totally ordinary birthday. No one has ever before offered me an eternal resting-place for one hundred dollars down and 8 percent interest.

In between my friends' phone calls and congratulations there was a real-estate lady who informed me that I now was too old to live in a big house and that she knew for sure that I dreamed about moving into a downtown condominium with no worries and one and one-half bathrooms. She further had a young couple ready to move into my house. It was all so easy.

I told her that I had no intention of moving because... And that is where I made my mistake. You should never argue with a saleslady on commission. Just put down the receiver while she is still engaged in her sales pitch. That little click saves many words and worries.

She was not the only one who called or faxed. I learned a lot during the following months. I learned to defend myself. A little awkwardly in the beginning but I became pretty good after a while.

The family dinner on my birthday was perfect. I got kisses and bear hugs and more kisses. The food was excellent and I marvelled at the happy young faces around the dinner table when one of the youngest declared:

– My teacher says that if you are a grandmother, you are old and then you will soon become an angel and fly up to heaven. And there I think you can eat all the ice cream you want and chocolate too.

That sounded good to him. He was smiling. I was a little overwhelmed. But I prefer that vision to the one the salesman painted with a view from a plot where I permanently rested my weary legs... It also made me realize how lucky I was and how much I have to be grateful for. So I am a senior! The number of my birthdays dictates that, but I am only one day older than yesterday. I am able to feel joy and contentment. I can taste the sweetness of life.

Old age can wait.

Old age can wait a long, long time yet.

Chapter 2

SIGNS OF OLD AGE

Something happens as the years go by. We can try to hide it, even deny it, but we know it is there. A certain deterioration, a subtle rusty feeling of decay.

Blame it on the mirrors. They are not what they used to be. The face that meets you when you shave or apply your make-up is different. A stranger is looking back at you, a ridiculous unrelated person with lines, wrinkles, and crow's-feet, small waves and a curly winding road down the cheeks you have never seen before. There can even be brown spots and the very beginning of an extra chin. There is destruction going on in the face you call yours.

Men will grow a beard as a cover-up, insisting that it has always been their dream to conceal the face with hair that constantly needs trimming and cleaning and attention and continually gets in the way, while women will spend a fortune on wonder creams that promise eternal wrinkle-free youth.

They work perfectly as long as you are on the right side of 30... We avoid sharp sunshine and hope this nightmare will be over soon. One morning in the future we pray to meet the face we know in the mirror that refuses to cooperate.

What to do! Oh, what to do!

The cheapest and safest is to get rid of all the mirrors in your home. It is a little hard to explain when the family comes around but it liberates you from the daily shocking, sinking feeling when you gaze at an old face looking back at you in your own bathroom.

– Mom, what happened to your mirrors? Why have you taken them down? Do you need to have them redone?

– Yes... They were... You are just about to say that the mirrors were old but somehow you cannot get that word over your lips.

However, that thin excuse for an explanation will only last a week.

– Dad, when are you getting your mirrors back and why have you not shaved? It is not like you.

Another week passes with some difficulty.

– Mom, you want me to phone the repairman? You should have your mirrors back by now. Dad, don't you think you should invest in a new shaver? It is your birthday soon. We could all...

– Mom, I think that company is taking advantage of you, my girlfriend's mother had the same trouble. She just cannot get her mirrors back.

There is something in that young voice that tells you that you have been found out or someone is on the right track.

The next day you decide to take the mirrors to a specialist. No stone should be left unturned.

He shakes his head.

– Lady, there is nothing wrong with that mirror. I have another senior customer who thinks...

– Never mind. I just thought...

The battle is lost, and the war just commenced.

Emmeline, my faithful friend and sister senior told me in confidence that she covers all her mirrors with sheets or towels according to size.

–The trick is to remove the covers when company is coming.

What a brilliant idea! Emmeline is full of brilliant ideas, and a few of them really work.

– Mom, why is there a pink towel over the mirror in the bathroom?

– Oh, I cleaned the walls...

You never used to tell fibs. You are ashamed and the youngster does not believe you anyway, so why bother? As a matter of fact, she will probably discuss you and your pink towel with her youngish husband that night.

– Mom is getting a little queer. I wonder why.

– Your mom is getting old, will be his merciless, thoughtless and true answer.

So let us discard Emmeline's brilliant idea. Leave the mirror on the wall although it insists that you no longer are the fairest of them all. Nature compensates in its own way.

As we grow older our eyes fail to pick up all the details. You discover that after a successful cataract operation, but then you are so happy that you do not have to give up your driver's license that the wrinkles and liverspots are not major issues. The face is really not so bad. It has a new charm, it shows wisdom, gentleness and experience. An older face has that special attraction and magnetism. We just have to get used to it. Remember all the people who love it, wrinkles and all. There is more to a person than a face, and as we get older we comprehend the old saying about the depth of beauty. We more or less have to.

It is not only the face that shows we have received that brown envelope from the government. The legs get weary, the hips seem to spread, the waistband needs an extra piece of elastic to be more comfortable, the shoes shrink during the day and are very, very tight at nightfall. It is so much trouble to put on a pair of boots. The arms must have shortened when you were not paying attention.

– Would you like a chair or a stool, dear?
The hostess must have noticed your trouble.

– Nonononono. I am fine. Thank you anyway, dear.
You are determined to get into your boots standing up, leaning ever so lightly against a wall, but standing, red-faced and out of breath. Vanity and stupidity are sisters by birth.

– It is much easier if you sit down. I have the same trouble, tries the hostess.

– What trouble! You are a little ashamed of yourself. It is not a Herculean task or a Gordian knot. It is just a pair of boots and you have lost a bit of balance over the years just as you have gained a few pounds around your midriff.

– Are you sure these boots are mine? Has someone else...

One boot is almost in place. The hostess watches discreetly or not so discreetly. The whole party does. There is nothing more difficult that trying to put on a pair of boots standing up while an audience is watching your silly private battle.

Ten minutes later the Pyrrhic victory is yours. The boots are where boots are supposed to be to do some good, but your back hurts and will do so for days.

Yes, we get a little juvenile. It is so darned hard to say – Could I please have a chair. I have trouble getting into my boots lately.

– Of course, dear. We are not getting any younger.

That means we are getting old.

Swallow twice and shut your mouth. No answer is necessary. Park your clever defense. Get on with your boot business. It will only take a minute, now that you are sitting down. We are all getting older, but that does not mean we are all hitting old age, unless we let it.

There is also this bizarre and nondescript feeling that the world is spinning at a faster pace and getting more complicated day by day.

It is. So what!

– But I do not want anyone to think that I am not right up there, understanding and comprehending new trends, modern innovations, new-fangled ideas, says Sophie with anger in her voice.

– I always did. Not that I liked them all. Nono. The young have their own lingo. Sometimes it is hard to understand what they mean, but sooner or later I managed. Now... She throws up her bony hands in disgust.

–You should hear them when they come over for Sunday dinner with their parents.

– Sophie, I hear them and I do not even pretend to know what they are talking about, so I ask questions. I say – 'scuse me, but what is a thing-a-ma-jig on the website?

– Granny, it is... They are eager to demonstrate their knowledge. And I remember when my grandfather refused to believe that a picture, a moving picture to boot, could appear in our living room. A sound, yes. But a picture, something called television... Absolutely not.

He was born when letters were literally carried by ponies, not by snails, and some people believed automobiles had no future. He grew up with wooden burners that had to be stoked and the belief that if a train moved faster than 25 miles an hour it would derail. He could not embrace the thought that a picture from somewhere could appear in his living room on his command.

But he was certainly not afraid to ask, and I was delighted and honoured to supply the answers. He was a wise old man. His experience and patience helped us when we were kids, eager to learn. Now it was payback time because he wanted to know. He was not afraid to show his shortcomings. He certainly did not sit with a closed mind and tight lips, wondering if the world was going to pot. He had not decided that it was all madness, sheer unadulterated madness and insanity. He asked and he got answers. Yes, he was a wise man.

Now it is our turn to ask.

– What was that again? But... Oh yes...

There is no generation gap as long as we talk to each other. Each generation has its own language. My mother complained – I wish you would express yourself without all that slang... Her mother probably said the same a generation earlier. There is no reason to feel old because your slang belongs to yesterday or yesteryear.

The legs are not what they used to be. The shopping malls are getting bigger, even the ones you visit frequently, and every one mumbles, swallows the words and makes it impossible to follow a conversation.

– Excuse me... I beg your pardon... What was that again...?

There are hearing aids for those of us in need.

– Hearing aid! Just the thought can cause otherwise reasonable people to explode. – I do not need a hearing aid. People should talk more clearly. Today everyone is in a rush and has no time to talk properly.

We do not mind glasses so we can see better, but let someone suggest a hearing aid or a cane.

– Me! A cane! Whatever for?

We want to age with dignity and grace, we want to continue enjoying life but some of us stubbornly refuse the assistance available. We rush towards old age because of our own stupidity and inflexibility. In order to delight in life we have to use our common sense, and it dictates the use of all available support as it becomes vital.

But, of course, we have choices. That is what life is all about. Choices. Do we want to enjoy getting older or do we just want to be miserable and complain. Everyone wants to live a long time but nobody wants to get old.

The three signs of aging are loss of memory and the other two I can't remember.

– I am old enough to admit that I am getting older, a wise senior said.

– What did you say, his compatriot asked.

– Never mind...

– What...

End of story.

Chapter 3

A WEDDING

We were all invited to the wedding – the bridge club, the choir, the knitting bee and the neighbours. Not that it was going to be a huge wedding, partly because members of the bridge club sing in the choir who again came to the knitting bee because they are neighbours. Still, a wedding is a wedding, especially among seniors.

There were times in our lives when we seemed to go from wedding to wedding. First round was when we were very young and everyone got married, including ourselves. That was the time when only a few, a very few lived together without official papers.

– You mean you could not get a chick to move in, or a guy?

My grandchildren's eyes are huge with doubt. – That must have been a hundred years ago, at least.

Not a hundred years, but it seems to belong to another world, with different standards and morals... I dislike to be reminded, but there it is, and I remember the disgust and the savage whispering.

– Have you heard that Anne...

– You don't say. Is she expecting?

– She should know better. Her dad is a teacher and her parents go to church every Sunday.

– Such a shame... Are you sure?

– Heard her telling someone else... Her parents threw her out... They had to, you know. Her dad is a member of the church board.

– Of course. Who do you think will marry her now? I mean when he gets tired of her.

Deep silence.

No one said – Who will marry that guy when Anne gets tired of him?

This gender difference is a solid part of our culture and no legislation can erase it. A husband has a fling or two and, if discovered, the wife is supposed to forget and forgive and take him back with open arms and a load of understanding. But even in our day, if the wife steps out of line, the sky is falling.

– There was a time when people believed that a marriage was created in heaven. There was a time when there were no computers or fast food or TV or condoms, I start explaining to the very young generation, but it has lost interest in the Stone Age. I think they wonder how we survived or if I am telling a fib.

I can hear my mother yet. – What do you mean they are going to be married next month? They have only known each other a year or so. That is an almost indecent haste... When I was young...

– Yes, a hundred years ago, I thought.

– Has he been presented to the family? Has there been an engagement party? Has he paid his respects to the aunts and the uncles? I do not understand what is going on nowadays. – My mother had a snake by the tail and would not let go. – How does he make a living? Does he earn enough to support a wife and children...?

This could go on for quite some time.

Never mind. That was then and it has nothing to do with the beautiful invitations we all received that morning – only I wondered what my mother would have said. Two of our old friends, two seniors were going to tie the eternal ribbon. Would she have frowned or would she have delighted in their happiness. I don't know. I cannot remember that two older people got married when I was a child. I don't think it was done. I could be wrong though.

Anyway, this was going to be an old-fashioned marriage, a church celebration with flowers and music and tears and wet handkerchiefs edged with handmade lace. How lovely. How absolutely delightful. They would stand at the altar with stars in their eyes and when the minister declared them to be man and wife, Mabel Smith – our dear friend, a member of the knitting bee and the choir and the bridge club, would be Mrs. Harold Brown.

– He is an only child, Emmeline informed us the morning the knitting bee gathered to finish some baby boots, not for Mabel, though, but for unwed mothers in the neighbourhood. The bride-to-be had discretely chosen to go shopping so we could discuss in peace the mutual gift, what we should wear when the big day arrived, and other details connected with the forthcoming event.

– An only child. How sad, said Sue-Marguerite. She has 14 siblings, and 11 children produced in three marriages with all three husbands decently buried one by one, side by side in the same family plot. – It should not be allowed to have only one child. Sue-Marguerite folded her scrawny hands, looking like a tired angel, and a little bit envious.

No one took up the debate. We were gathered on this day to discuss apparel and flowers and a gift – and to drink coffee, of course. It would be a long morning without crossing swords over family volumes.

– Mabel is going to be in pink. She feels it is her colour and I agree with her. Pink is always elegant and at the same time discreet, if it is the right shade. So I think we all should avoid pink. We do not want to compete with the bride, be it ever so subtle – Mary said.

Each group has its own general, whether it knows it or not. We have General Mary, a stout well-corseted lady with a prominent nose and a voice that can cut through any noise. She had once in her very young days been the co-ordinator of a fashion show when the Maple Leaf Ladies' Society in the town where she lived, convinced her to take on that job in order to raise money for Christmas gifts the poor would enjoy. It was many, many years ago and I do not know if the fashion show was a success or the poor enjoyed their gifts but from that day on Mary was the expert when it came to fashion, and when she declared that none but the bride was allowed to wear pink at the forthcoming wedding, it was simply the law. You did not discuss with Mary. The general had given an order and the privates just obeyed.

It was, however, a bit of a shock and very close to a catastrophe for the members of the knitting bee, as it would be for the choir and the bridge club. It is no secret that we seniors swear on pink when it comes to a party dress. It is usually hanging at the back of the closet and only taken out of the bag once or twice a year for special occasions. It is good to know it is there. It gives peace of mind. But now General Mary had declared war on all pink dresses. Yes, it was a disaster.

We could, of course, ignore Mary and her expertise, but that was not easily done. Mary has sharp eyes. Even pink handkerchiefs would be outlawed. Her tongue is cutting, and she has the ability to convince others that she is right. Her dad was the local solicitor and her mother's dad was the best salesman in the county. Everybody used the pots and pans he represented. Mary never became a saleslady or a solicitor but she ruled her husband and their six offspring on a small farm with all its inconveniences. She knows how to convince a big group. Anyway, it is easier to agree with her and later go your own way. That is probably how her husband and the six children survived.

– No shades of pink, we repeated, prudently making virtue out of necessity.

– There are so many other colours in the rainbow, added Emmeline in a special, soft, goody-goody voice.

That point of the agenda taken care of, we discussed the wedding present, which General Mary had decided should be an ornament her cousin was selling for twenty percent off. She would, she promised, figure out down to the last cent how much it would be for each of us, including card, giftwrap and ribbons.

There was no dissension, no other suggestions and absolutely no discussion.

Emmeline's angelic smile made me nervous but I seemed to be the only one who noticed it.

– No pink shades, Emmeline repeated, and by now she looked like an archangel.

I moved uneasily in my chair and tried to figure out what Emmeline had in mind. But she just sat there with closed eyes and folded hands. Something was cooking. A tiny smile, a fleeting merriment lingered in the left corner of her mouth. When she felt she was unobserved, it spread to her face and became pure delight and anticipation. – Absolutely no shade of pink, she repeated with her cherubic smile.

The neat and delicate invitation, complete with two hearts in gold, and two angels silently but triumphantly blowing a horn each, said that the happy occasion would take place at two o'clock in the afternoon, with the reception commencing at six, so here was another problem, General Mary pointed out, although she already had the solution: It meant evening attire, she proclaimed. We nodded. Again.

We had a peaceful discussion about the transportation while drinking more coffee and chewing fresh danishes, dropping crumbs all over the sitting-room carpet which happened to be mine. Mary declared that she had the schedule figured out, and finished off by saying that everything would be *comme il faut*. When Mary starts speaking French, we know that she is satisfied with herself and her efforts. She learned that language in school from a Ukrainian teacher and luckily enough only remembers three or four phrases. *Comme il faut* is one of them. She uses it quite frequently. She seems to be on safe ground with *comme il faut*.

– No pink, repeated Mary.

I was sweating because Emmeline winked with one eye. We both thought of our pink best dress in the back of our closets.

The day came, with all its nervous goings-on. We all have the same hairdresser and we had all booked an 11 o'clock appointment. Celestine, the hair-witch had confirmed them all, which meant that someone had to wait for somebody, and the atmosphere was close to the boiling point before the group was able to leave the so-called beauty parlour with exactly the same coiffure because that is the only one Celestine knows and it is the quickest, which was of some importance that day.

Dresses had been hauled out from oblivion and pressed and checked for spots and pressed again, shoes had been inspected, the dainty party purse pulled out from the top drawer where it had rested since last time, which was quite a while ago. It was now stuffed to the brim with handkerchiefs; nylons had been selected, the right shade – not too dark and not too light, and hopefully without runs. The wedding party was indeed preparing itself. The few men were probably engaged in shaving and cursing, but at least they had no problem with the colour pink.

The weather was warm and cozy, so was a coat in style, or would a shawl be enough? We all decided on a coat. The weather might change, and some had seen a little dark cloud sailing over the blue sky. At least, that was our excuse for the coats.

It was Emmeline's turn to pick me up according to Mary's schedule. She had washed her car carefully and vacuum-cleaned it, even polished the windows. She told me that over the phone at the time that she should have been at my door. Everything was up to scratch, she said, only the car would not start. Perhaps because she had washed it.

That meant that I had to pick her up and hurry in order to get to the church on time. My car started fine but it was not washed. It was grubby, with layers of dust that covered the colour and the rust. It was really not a car you wanted to park in front of a church, or later to participate in the wedding procession. But we had no choice and we managed to hide it four blocks behind the church on a quiet street where no one recognized us.

We reached the holy place half a minute before the ceremony commenced, red-faced and short of breath, still with our coats on.

– Did you walk to church? Mary asked, although we had tried to avoid her.

– Only the last seven blocks, Emmeline smiled, and she again looked like an angel.

The sun was shining and it was rather warm, but all the ladies of the collected choir, bridge club and knitting bee kept their coats on and looked suspiciously guilty doing so. Not a sliver of pink was seen, and Mary smiled with satisfaction.

Music filled the room and here came Mabel Smith with her husband-to-be, Harold Brown, hand in hand, slowly up the aisle, carefully leaning towards each other, stopping now and then to quiet the heartbeat or breathe deeply. After all, the bride was 77 and the groom 82, but we did not for a moment think about their age because they looked so happy. The groom had a solid cane in his free hand and his back was stooped but he seemed to straighten himself as he came closer to the altar. The bride looked absolutely adorable in a light grey suit and a creamy hat with blue adornment. Before the couple reached the final goal, all coats seemed to disappear and the church was suddenly a small sea of pink, and there sat Emmeline with her angelic smile and her folded hands and had a very good time studying General Mary's face...

– Mabel told me she had changed her colour scheme, Emmeline whispered so everyone could hear it – and I let a word fall here and there.

Only General Mary was in cream and gold and looked as if she did not quite belong.

The bride and the groom resided in the same nursing home. It was here they met and it was here we celebrated their union with coffee and a wedding cake and alcohol-free punch. We wished the happy couple a long life together and we all got rather noisy, which surprised the manager of the establishment, but then he did not know the contents of Emmeline's brown bag, which she discreetly emptied into the bowl containing the alcohol-free punch so it all of a sudden had a lot of punch!

General Mary toasted the bride. She always makes speeches on our behalf and she it pretty good at it but that evening she went a little overboard when she lifted her glass and declared she would be a faithful godmother when the time came. We all laughed and the General joined in the merriment, and Emmeline looked more saintly than ever.

Later when the tables were removed by the janitor on overtime, we danced. Somebody played the piano and we could hear it now and then, but mostly we sang and had a jolly good time. The whole nursing home was invited. There must have been 30 ladies and three men. It worked out fine, thanks to Emmeline's innovation. The groom fell asleep in a wheelchair but that did not bother the new Mrs. Harold Brown. She danced with grace and vigor with the janitor, who drank his share of the punch. When she tired of a long and eventful day and fell asleep in another wheelchair we carefully and tenderly pushed her and her groom back to their rooms. Harold's was in the north end of the nursing home and Mabel's straight south. They both looked content and fulfilled.

– It will be six dollars and seventy-one cents for each, General Mary reminded us.

– Whatever for? Emmeline was in high spirit. She did not have to drive home.

– For the ornament minus twenty percent. –

– They have neither room nor use for an ornament. Return it. The choir and the bridge club and especially the knitting bee showed courage for once.

Honestly, I do not remember what we decided to do, but I do recall that we danced down the narrow hallway like a long pinkish snake. We took a taxi home.

The driver smiled when Emmeline and I started singing. I am not sure we were on the same page.

      – A good party.

      – The best. A wedding.

      – A young romance...

      – Just a romance.

We laughed, Emmeline and I, two happy seniors with no thoughts of old age.

Chapter 4

GRANDFATHER HAS A GIRLFRIEND

How does a 75-year-old father and grandfather inform his family that his girlfriend is moving in for good?

Well, as long as you are prepared for battle, you just tell.

– Dad, are you crazy? You must be joking. Are you completely out of your mind!

A daughter in her mid-life crisis usually leads the attack.

– No. I am not joking. Adelina has sold her house and will move in next month.

It feels a little silly that you have to defend yourself, almost ask for permission to live your life the way you want to. It is because you are a senior and the world seems to have procured the right to adjudicate your actions, judge your performance and in some cases cancel a license.

– You are grounded, Daddy. Go to your room and think it over.

The roles are so reversed. Not that the children and in-laws say those words, but they might as well. Shadow dancing is very tiresome.

The first bullet is usually – What would mom have said?

The air is heavy with memories and sentimentality. The blow is below the belt. Everyone knows it and everyone does it.

– Your mother has been dead for more than 7 years, my dear.

– What a cruel thing to say. Have your already forgotten her? We all loved her. You most of all. And now you will allow a strange woman to take her place.

At this time a few tears trickle down someone's cheek.

If you are weak or if you have second thoughts about Adelina, it is the right time to open your arms and cradle your weeping daughter to your hairy bosom. Peace on earth. All is well with the world. You can go back to long lonely evenings and nights, talk to yourself because there is no one else to talk to, and drown in self-pity, admitting you are close to old age and you deserve to be in that lonesome cell.

– You have us, Daddy. The tears are really flowing.

Do not believe that for a moment. You have yourself and no one else. Your family, your daughters, sons, in-laws and grandchildren have their own lives. It is how it should be, and if you are a coward and do not dare to take a chance with Adelina, you will suffer. The others will just go on with their lives.

– I am so glad I convinced Dad to give up Adelina. I mean at his age!

Douse your contentment. Your action is despicable. You have condemned your dad to old age, with all its complications. Leave him alone to live his own life. He only has one.

It is, of course, just as much daddy's fault that he does not stand up to the family and ask the whole bunch to mind their own business.

– All right. I shall rephrase. Your mother, my wife, passed away more than 7 years ago in her sleep. There was no foul play. She was in the hospital, even in

49

a real bed in a regular room. It was not one of these gurney situations in an overcrowded emergency room. She had a stroke. She was monitored by experts. I spent three days and four nights at her bedside and lived on hospital hamburgers and yellow mustard plus something they insisted was coffee. I slept in the chair, I hardly left her. I wanted to be certain she got the right treatment. You kids phoned now and then, if I remember correctly…

– We were busy and the nurse said there was nothing we could do anyway.

– Please do not interrupt. I have the floor.

– How can you joke...

– Silence! Your mother and I had a good marriage. We liked each other and that is sometimes more important than loving each other. I hope you know the feeling and the difference.

It was not your mother's first stroke, but this one would have left her a complete invalid, depending on others in all situations. Your mother would have hated that. You know it. I know it. She was smart, intelligent, good-looking. She had the right to pass away at that moment when we remembered her with all her faculties up to par. She had the right to die and she did. May her soul rest in peace. Mercifully her heart stopped while she was still in a coma. I missed her. Life had not the same meaning for a long, long time, but that was then. Adelina is now.

– Dad, you can't be serious. A short hard laugh comes and goes. – Look at you...

– I do that every morning when I shave...

– You are 75, almost bald and at least 20 pounds overweight. On top of that you shake... Your hands...

– So does Adelina. We met in a support group for shakers. Not movers and shakers. Just shakers. They all shake for different reasons and in different degrees. That is part of the beauty of our affair. We do not have to try to hide it. We are not ashamed...

– Your affair...

There you are, feeling youngish and vital. You have an affair!

You danced with Adelina at the institution where shakers meet twice a month to convince themselves that they can live a normal life even if they cannot control their movements at will. Two hearty and heavy nurses are in attendance, dressed in too-tight sweaters and slacks with no room for expansion. Two well-meaning ladies who will clap their hands and stamp their feet in order to convince everybody that this is just an ordinary get-together for ordinary seniors.

– Alex... You will dance with Adelina.

You were actually tired, but stout nurses have their own way of getting their own way.

– Of course. You smiled and Adelina smiled back.

Her smile was warm and so natural. Not just a grimace. You forgot for a moment that this was not an ordinary dance for ordinary seniors. Heads and legs, arms, fingers and feet were constantly engaged in involuntary movements that never seemed to stop.

You danced with Adelina the first time because you were told to do so. The second time was your own choice.

You saw her home in the wintry afternoon when the bleak sun already had left the horizon. You felt rich and content. It was such a long time since you had seen a lady home. She made coffee. Good strong coffee, just as you like it. You enjoyed that and you enjoyed her. She was a neat little person with an optimistic outlook. She did not expect too much from this world and was thankful for what she received. You had not been so relaxed and so content for many years. You leaned back in the deep chair, enjoying the feeling and the moment. Your hands were still shaking, actually from the elbows down, but no one suggested that you should try to control them.

– Honestly, Daddy. You could try a little harder. It makes everybody very nervous. And what a mess. Look at the tablecloth. Dr. Smith says that you should not shake that much if you take your pills on time. Have you forgotten...?

– Dad, how can you even think about going to Uncle Henry's birthday. You shake and you will make a mess. It is a dinner party and no one would like to sit next to you, and Aunt Nellie is so particular. Unless, of course, you let Dr. Smith prescribe some stronger pills. Even if you feel nauseated you will not shake, and they will carry you through the dinner without a disaster. I will phone Auntie Nellie for you. She will understand your apologies.

Sitting in Adelina's comfortable chair in her neat living room, you remember all that talk about your shakes. When you go to your daughter's for supper, it is now served in the kitchen. There is even an extra towel at your place. A bib! Eating with a bib. You stopped going there because you felt so degraded, so disgraced, almost dishonoured. The grandchildren must have been instructed not to make any comments, but their young curious inquisitive eyes follow every movement of your unsteady hands. You try to smile, to establish a bond you so often have done before when you wanted them to know that some grown-ups are hilariously demanding – but the children do not smile back. They just look as if you were a stranger, a queer one landed at their supper table by mistake.

– Ooops... Never mind, Dad. Your daughter's voice is so condescending and overbearing.

You found an excuse when you were invited. You deliberately invented one and you were thankful but very hurt because they pretended to believe you. They come and visit now and then, always between meals. You are not a naive idiot.

– Gosh, Adelina, I spilled some coffee on your beautiful rug...

– Not to worry, dear. Everything in this house is washable. I have had the shakes for years. You learn not to let it dictate your lifestyle. You compensate.

Remember how she laughed and you liked her laughter. You leaned forward to study her closely and you liked what you saw. Outside, darkness was complete and it had started to snow. The wind kicked up a leg and howled in the chimney. You stayed the night. As a matter of fact, you stayed two nights. And enjoyed everything.

The third night you took a taxi home in order to be at the right place when a volunteer driver would come the next morning and pick you up for a doctor's appointment and later escort you to the dance where you could sway away the afternoon with Adelina in your shaking arms.

One day Adelina presented her son. His name was Jim and he had a good laugh. He liked beer and stayed until there were no more left, which was about an hour.

– I try not to have more than three bottles in the house, Adelina said, and you sat in the lazy chair and had fun talking to Jim, who did not seem to notice your shakes, and talked about old cars and ice hockey and not about anti- shaking drugs.

You should introduce Adelina to your own family. Perhaps she was wondering. She never mentioned it, and your eyes are too weak to read her silent feeling.

– Would you like to meet my daughter?

– If it is convenient…

That was when you decided to tell the world about your affair.

So far the conversation developed exactly as you knew it would. Your shaking was brought forward as usual. That monster always takes center-stage. Your whole life seems to circle around your disability. But there is so much more to life. Adelina has taught you that.

– Listen, kiddo. – You eye your 50-year-old daughter with love, fatherly concern and a grain of pity. – I know I am 75, overweight and almost bald. I certainly know I have the shakes. I never have a chance to forget it except when I am with Adelina.

– Is she blind?

– No, I don't think so. But she makes me forget. I am very comfortable with Adelina, and my mind is made up.

– You mean you are going to marry her.

– I wouldn't mind, but that is just a small detail. A piece of paper. Your laughter is deep and good.

– You really mean that you and this woman...

– This woman has a name, and you better learn it because she means lot to me. But at our age a piece of paper is not the most important thing. We take a day at a time and enjoy what it has to offer. The days are short and only God knows how many are left...

– But what will other people think?

– I just told you how unimportant that is.

– I never thought that my children's grandfather would have a girlfriend...

– Get used to the thought.

– I wish you had never told me, Dad.

– I wanted you to know. I want you to meet Adelina. She is not a dirty secret... She is an important part of my life.

Your voice is victorious and happy.

When Alec told me about Adelina and his family's reluctance to accept her, I cheered him on his way. I also remembered a day not so long ago when a good friend phoned me in panic one morning and sobbed over the phone.

– Can you drive me to a funeral? she managed to say.

– Of course. When? Who died?

It turned out to be that very day and in Calgary, about 4 hours' driving from door to door. Bea did not say a word on the way down. She insisted on paying her respects without me. She wept all the way back – another 4 hours' drive.

Just before Leduc she said – I loved him and he loved me. We just kept it a secret, a little ashamed of our feelings, I suppose. What would our families say? I felt so alone today. I was all by myself. No one knew who I was. I read about his death this morning in the newspaper. I wish we had told everybody. Just because you are getting older, you have not lost the right to love.

Indeed not. You have earned it.

Love is such a splendid feeling. It belongs to all ages.

Chapter 5

JOIN A CHOIR

Yes, yes, yes. Join a choir. Sing, sing, sing and feel alive. There is nothing like it. A choir is the answer if you feel alone, left out, or a little on the downside of life. Even a little old.

I know there are bridge clubs and book clubs and knitting bees and a lot of other activities if you look for them, but most of them have a set programme. You know exactly what will happen.

Our knitting bee is very useful. We knit for young mothers and their beautiful babies. That is a good thing and we will never give it up. But if we examine what we do apart from the knitting we have to admit that we know the agenda from a to z. We come, we knit, we small-talk, we drink coffee and eat too many sweets because they are so good except for our health and figure.

We gossip and we drink some more coffee, get a few new patterns and then we go home. There is nothing really exciting about the whole process, nothing that takes you out of your everyday living, uplifts you and makes you forget your general worries. Nothing you can take home and live on for a while, except perhaps the tid-bits of juicy gossip, and that you could have familiarized yourself with over the phone in half an hour with the right person.

The bridge club is no better in that regard. There is, of course, not much time for gossiping because most of the members are so serious about their cards and the way they should be played. You really cannot relax for a moment, and your shortcomings are discussed and dissected for months to come.

– We had a slam, if you only...

– How on earth could you say four with only...

Oh, the mistakes you can make and the constant judgement of your intelligence and ability to handle 13 cards.

Some people love it and have warm hands every day from playing. Some of us are only there because there has to be four people around the table, and we know we are the last resort.

Book clubs are mostly serious business where you are out to prove the depth of your soul. Five or ten people are gathered to demonstrate they cannot only read but they understand the written word and the author, often much better than the author understands him- or herself.

– She was depressed when she wrote that paragraph... He must have been between lovers... It is clear she did not have a happy childhood...

And then there is this eternal discussion when the next book has to be decided upon.

– Let us have something light. Something that makes us laugh.

But the learned and intelligent core of the club will not allow that. You have to plough through pages of words you do not comprehend. Sometimes you wonder if the author has invested too much time and money in the latest thesaurus. The people in the book are not normal. They do all kinds of disgusting things. You are immersed in their sickness, their stupidity, unhappiness, shame and disgrace. After three pages you have had enough. You sit silently and listen when the book club gets together next time. They seldom discuss the first three pages at any length.

It is not very uplifting, it is rather depressing. You almost drown in the meanness of the world and you try to remind yourself that you joined for the fun of it.

Well, that is for some people, and they love it.

To be a member of a choir is quite different. Where, may I ask, are so many and such different activities collected under one name. Choirs have dinners and dances and committees and discussions and singing. The members constantly call each other, drive each other and care for each other. They laugh and cry and are not afraid of their feelings. They eat together and sing together and some of them sleep together, but that is their own business as long as they remember to be present at rehearsals. To join a choir is a sure way of enjoying life to its fullest at any age.

Some choirs have auditions because it is an advantage if the members can carry a tune; most seniors' choirs will accept you with open arms. There is always something you can do if your voice is not up to its earlier power. Some seniors, some rather old seniors still sing with all the beauty and innocence of a twenty-year-old. It is amazing. It is simply wonderful. Sometimes some of us make funny noises where they are not wanted but there is no need to worry. Our comrades in arms will carry us through. Nobody will suggest discretely that you take up crocheting or woodwork instead of singing, or just look after the coffee from now on. No one will scold you or make jokes, some of them can't even hear their mistakes.

In order to join a mature choir it is best to have a voice, but once I was a valued member under the condition that I just open my mouth and silently followed what the rest were doing.

– We need some tall people. We are out to quell the myth that all seniors are little old ladies, the choirmaster told me.

So there I was in a whitechapel blue dress. I stood tall and straight in the third row and only once did I overstep my assignment and raised my voice. Luckily the trumpets and the percussion at the same time had a private competition, so no one heard me and my mistake.

If the conductor decides you are an alto, you are an alto because one more alto is needed in the choir. Later you can discreetly move into the row of the second sopranos provided you get the right sheets of music. Most choirs, however, are overloaded with second sopranos and bassos; that deep manly voice tends to take over. Some of them are promoted to baritones but they still have the same voice.

There is something about singing and blending your voice with other voices that makes you happy and gives you a feeling of joy, pleasure, zest and satisfaction. Forgotten are the grey hours and worries and even the thought that you should have let the dog out before you left. You open your mouth and you sing, you bask in the sunshine you share with the group, you tread on enchanted ground. It is sheer happiness and bliss.

There are lots of rehearsals and they lead to concerts – in most cases. When Christmas or Easter approaches, your choir is in great demand. There are dozens and dozens of nursing homes and shopping malls looking for seasonal entertainment that will bring the soldiers out in the right mood. A choir is not too overly exciting, it does not invite uncontrolled behaviour. People will not go wild and do funny things. With a choir of seniors, one is on the safe side.

No one realizes how many lodges and nursing homes there are in the vicinity until one belongs to a choir, a volunteer choir, and Christmas is in the air. Two or three people are occupied solely with engagements of that sort – mostly second sopranos or bassos. They rewrite the schedule a dozen times and their efforts are very much appreciated. The rehearsals for the Christmas season start months ahead of time. So does the discussion or the battle about what to wear at the concerts. I remember one year where the ladies rebelled en masse because we were tired of white blouses and black skirts. We wanted something daring, low-cut and flamboyant. The gentlemen smacked their lips and seconded the motion with a glint in their eyes. It took three meetings to decide that the colour should not be mauve because it was unbecoming in electric light and at Christmastime you cannot rely on the sun, especially at eventide. Concurrently we tried to find out which day of the week would be convenient for everyone to rehearse, and at what time, if we managed to find a desirable weekday.

All singers have the gift of the gab, and plead their case and cause with conviction and eloquence. The coffee committee worked overtime. In the end we decided to meet on Tuesdays as usual and at two o'clock in the afternoon as we have always done. The ladies were back to their decent white blouses and black pleaded skirts. One year earrings were allowed, but that by-law was hastily scrapped as too many lost one during the concert and were seen crawling around on the stage during intermission in order to locate their treasure.

Some people should never be seen crawling around on a stage on all fours. The audience howled with laughter and applauded loudly. Some thought it was part of the entertainment. There was even a call for an encore when Rosie, our best soprano and star of the evening, who can hit a high C with a vengeance, got stuck in between two chairs. She wriggled herself loose, but we all knew she was not really looking for an earring but for the first tenor's hands, or any part of his body for that matter. Anyway, her underwear was blue with pink laces, and everyone had a good look. Everyone who could see that is. She found a basso, which was not appreciated by his wife as much as it was by him. So the earrings were scratched shortly after that episode – moved, seconded, and carried single-handedly by the basso's good woman.

At the fifth rehearsal, the choice of music was brought forward by the conductor, who already had decided on our behalf. Each day brought us closer to Christmas, he said, and no one could argue with that statement.

There is so much wonderful music in this world. One does not really know how much until one joins a choir and all forty-two members pursue their own favourites with vim and vigour. There is always a rather conservative group who will not budge from 'Oh Holy Night'. If this group is headed by the tenor or the best soprano, it is recommended that the fight be given up right away. Both have the power and the voice to destroy your choices. If you want a battle, pick one with the altos and the bassos. In the long run, we all had to compromise. And in the end you still sing the conductor's choice.

Christmas concerts rest peacefully on tradition, as they should. The younger and more adventuresome part of the senior choir will have to fall in line, which it always does. There were never any casualties during those debates; there were perplexing reasoning, unreliable analysis, debatable polemics, but never any death or broken limbs, and they all ended in coffee with or without cream, depending on the entertainment committee's reliability and memory.

The conductor, who sometimes is the only one who can read music, will tactfully suggest that we start singing because that is why we are here, and a good battle-scarred conductor with some experience will choose a well-known Christmas carol to calm everyone down and unite the fighting groups. Thus the first rehearsal has commenced.

The conductor has already secured a place in heaven at a later date just by being Maestro. He or she has to be tactful, able to smooth easily ruffled feathers, patient, smiling, firm and yet flexible, thoughtful, always on time, and with a solid knowledge of music. The conductor can expect phone calls early in the morning and late at night from people with a better idea. The conductor must be a saint.

Before you know it, Christmas is upon us… It happens every year. Was it not yesterday we raked the leaves in the yard and the wind gracefully lifted them onto the neighbour's driveway – with a little help from your own rake. The same wind lifted them back in front of your door when it decided to change and perhaps the neighbour was outside with his rake. But it could not have been yesterday, because now the days are very short and darkness falls in the middle of the morning.

If it would only snow. It will. At least in Western Canada. Wish for snow and you shall have it, for the next six months. Life is not predictable out here. The weather is not predictable either. But the snow is. Winter comes and when it is darkest and coldest and most miserable, a star is born, a bright star with hope and comfort for the grey masses. Christmas! The choirs are pining to go at least six weeks before the brightest night.

Our pre-Christmas schedule has been plastered on the wall for a good long time. Now action begins. We are rooted out of the trenches up onto the stages, and received with open arms and clapping hands, and old people now and then fall asleep in their wheel chairs because their bones are tired. But they enjoy the choirs. They remember Christmas long ago, and a tear rolls slowly down a scruffy wrinkled cheek. They fall asleep again, but with a little smile in the corner of thin dry lips. We have not worked in vain. We are bringing something to them that cannot be bought or wrapped. The joy of Christmas. The spirit of the holy season.

A last bow and we are on the road again to the next lodge, the next nursing home, the next shopping mall.

– Does anybody know where we are going now? The leading car belongs to the leading tenor. – Where is the schedule?

– On the wall back at the rehearsal room!

– For Pete's sake...

– Who has a phone...?

Four people raise their hands.

– Who has the telephone number?

Dead silence.

But Lucy is there and she always knows what to do. She is never without suggestions and some kind of a solution.

– My aunt will know. She knows everything about our choir. I will phone auntie. Just give me a phone. Thank you. Aunt Beth, is that you? Yes, it is me. How are you, Auntie? Ready for Christmas? Oh, that is too bad. No, I agree. Just take it easy... That is always the best way... ...No, that is no substitute... And just before Christmas... I understand... Great Scot... So mean... Yes, yes, yes... Have you got the recipe?... I would just love to have it. Thank you so much. Take care, Auntie... Bye-bye...

– How come you did not ask her about our schedule?

– Her cat ran away. She thinks someone stole it. So mean. Just before Christmas. She could not find her glasses. I bet she forgot them at her boyfriend's place. Heck, she is only 67. Let her enjoy life while she can. No, she can't read anything without her glasses. It was no use asking her...

Somebody always recalls something – after a while.

– As far as I remember, we should be going to...

The leading tenor leads us onward in the winter darkness. Snow is falling and we are already half an hour late. We find the nursing home, only they did not expect us until the following evening, but they are so happy to see us. They will not let us go, now that we are there. We may forget to come tomorrow. We unpack and sing and drink weak juice and eat soft cookies. We sing again. Everybody sings. It is a delightful affair. Just beautiful.

It turned out that another choir landed where we should have been. They also had their schedule safely pasted to the wall in the rehearsal room so they knew where to find it.

We are, of course, volunteers. I doubt anyone will dole out cash for our performance. So if Aunt Mildred has invited you to her birthday party the same evening you are supposed to sing your heart out at a lodge, you know your duty. After all, you are only one small voice in a big choir, and Auntie Mildred is counting on you. She is family. You will join the choir's efforts at the next performance.

It can, however, have a profound influence on the sound effects if six sopranos are missing due to family affairs. The bassos are always the most faithful, and so it can happen that only two sopranos are left to do battle with 18 bassos and 14 altos. When that happens, we count on the audience's lack of hearing. The conductor will suffer, and meekly suggest at our next combined rehearsal and coffee party that we could let someone know we will be absent by phoning one of the phoners. We gladly agree. We love to phone each other, so his suggestion is passed with flying colours... We phone each other like mad over the next couple of weeks. Unfortunately most people forget to mention why they phoned. But we tried. That is all a person can do.

Those who have never belonged to a choir have no idea how much work goes on behind the curtain, so to speak. It is certainly not enough that a choir can sing, although it does help. There is music to be copied and distributed, preferably to the right voices, transportation, schedules, phoning, last minute changes, flowers to be ordered, speeches to be written, letters to be mailed, and a million other things, including nerves to be calmed. The most glaring mistakes are made by the transportation committee. I mean, it does not help one iota that we know the music and we are dressed as we should be, with the right song sheets in our hot little hands, and that we are all at the rehearsal room on time, if we cannot find our way out to the place we are supposed to serenade.

So why do we meet at the rehearsal place? Because we want to be quite sure that every one has a ride and no one gets lost.

All is well as long we all go to the same place the same night at the same time. But one evening our signals got completely crossed and the result was that half the choir went to a United Church on the north side of the river, while the other half parked outside a nursing home on the south side of the river. They both refused to budge because they both claimed the other half was wrong.

– Let us have no more of that nonsense, Adam said at the next rehearsal, and when Adam speaks, the crowd listens. Apart from his booming voice, his company supplies doughnuts and plastic cups all through the season.

– We drive to the venue in a convoy. That way we all end up at the same place.

That should work fine. We set out in good spirits down the Christmas-crowded Whyte Avenue. Adam was in the front. What could go wrong? His car was red as a tomato. My car was next, and I hung on to that four-wheeled tomato through traffic and pink lights like a burr, without knowing that another red car had broken the line. The black car with Emmeline was right behind me. We ended up at the International Airport, and even I knew we had nothing to do there and something was wrong.

A lady got out of the red car and waved good-bye to a man, and the red car disappeared into the night.

– What are we doing here? Emmeline had rolled down a window. She had the right to inquire. She also had the leading soprano in her car. – Shall we go on to Red Deer? Emmeline went on. She can be very cutting.

– Or Vancouver? one of my passengers quipped.

– Let us get back to the city and find where we are supposed to be, suggested the leading soprano, who also had a solo.

– I have no idea where we are supposed to be. I just followed Adam's red car, I thought.

We had a good laugh in the winter chill. That is what I adore about people who want to sing. They very seldom are mean or petty. They take everything in stride, and since we did not know where to go, we ended up in a bar, where the leading soprano entertained the crowd during happy hour. Huge success.

I had two good tenors in my car. Needless to say, we never tried that method of transportation again.

But other things could go wrong. The lady with all the music once got stuck on the High Level Bridge for two hours. The same night the accompanist disappeared in a snowstorm and the conductor could not start his car. He refused to stop trying until his battery was dead and there was no taxi in sight. We sang that night without music, without a conductor, and without an accompanist. It turned out to be a fair race, with the bassos winning as usual. They came in three bars before the rest.

We are still wearing white blouses and black skirts, and we are still discussing a change. We still get lost or forget the music sheets and sometimes some of us are even on the wrong page. But do we enjoy ourselves? Yes, we do, and it happens that other people enjoy us as well. They listen and they clap their hands and they look happy. That is all we ask. Perhaps they once were members of a choir. Perhaps they remember and they can't help smiling.

If you want to forget your age and your small or not-so-small worries and pains: join a choir. You will never regret it as long as you live.

Though old as the hills

If you count my years

My heart still harbours

A youthful laughter

Because I can taste

The sweetness of life

Chapter 6

HELP – I NEED HELP

As we gradually grow older and consequently slow down, mostly because we have to, and if we live in our own house and intend to stay there even though our grown-up children suggest once a week that we should move into a lodge, it is more than convenient to have a fellow who will come to our rescue and fix whatever needs fixing and who is preferably available 24 hours a day. He is called a handyman and that is exactly what he is.

The more modern gadgets we have, the more help we need, because all those electrical wonders have the peculiar habit of breaking down at the oddest moments when their domestic cooperation is most needed and wanted. When we had younger legs and keener eyes we could usually remedy the situation before disaster struck.

– There is water on the kitchen floor, dear.

– I can see that. Let's get cracking before it seeps into the basement. Shut off the main outlet, will you. It is probably just a broken hose.

Oh, those carefree days when you could hear and see and get down on your knees without worrying about how to get up again. We took care of everything in the house, otherwise we would not have been able to afford both it and the three children. There was no option.

The children have moved away now, at least for a while. It is very cool nowadays to take up residence with your parents again, bless them, with the attendance of your whole family, whether it is appreciated or not. It is also rather expensive – for the parents.

A funny thing is that when children move out for good, they usually settle a thousand kilometers away, very seldom down the street or two blocks over. It is good for the telephone company but not so smart when your eaves need cleaning.

– I will do it when I come out for the summer holidays. Junior can help me. He is almost 10 now. Don't worry, Dad.

The telephone system is tailor-made for broken promises.

You do worry, and you should. Summer is, after all, 5 months away.

– Wonder if we shouldn't try to get some help. The words leave your mouth reluctantly and grudgingly.

– To clean the house. That would be nice, dear. Your better half is all in favour.

– Well, perhaps that, and there is also the snow. It seems to fall every day...

– Oh, you mean a handyman. Perhaps he can fix the toilet and the kitchen sink and the drawer that doesn't work and...

There seems to be an absolute need for a handyman. But where to find him or her, the wonder with a patient smile and clever hands that can fix anything.

You seldom discover that phenomenon right away, but stick your toe in the water, gather your courage, and do something. Someone knows someone. That is what neighbours are for – among other things.

– Try Peter, one block over. He retired last month. His wife is going crazy.

– Perhaps Jim. He needs something to do.

– What about Wilma? Now there is a handy person.

Perhaps you are on your way to unveil a new miracle.

Try one of them out. Start with the eaves.

For that you need a long ladder, and it is sometimes a job for two. If you find yourself on top of the ladder, hanging on for dear life with one hand while you try to clean the eaves with the other, and your handyman is safely on the ground, lighting a cigarette and casually holding on to the ladder, I do not think you should engage that individual without further investigation. That person might have worked for the City.

I say that because I have experience in that regard. No, I never worked for the City, but lived once on a street where the local by-law officer came visiting on a daily basis on his way to and fro between his homestead and his desk. He just hated the sight of unshovelled snow on the sidewalks, so he really had a hard time six months of the year. He could have asked to be transferred to a milder climate with more rain than snow. Perhaps he tried but his good woman would not let him move. So his revenge was that he slapped warnings and fines around and watched with glee the pain in his brethren's faces.

Each city has its own by-laws, and if it snows a lot, it is vital to know them by heart. There are cities where you are not allowed to remove the snow from the sidewalks, mostly because it would just be shovelled onto the street, which is already full of the white stuff.

In our city, you have to clear the snow off the sidewalks right down to the pavement within 48 hours after the last snowfall. Otherwise you are a criminal and must be treated like one. You can appeal your fines – after you have paid.

It is always hard to determine when the snow stops falling.

Our city is sprawling, and the sky often clears from the west. The sun or the moon will appear there while we on the cheaper east side are still hoping for improvement from heaven above...

Our local by-law officer felt that what happened in the west end was good enough for the whole city – and we thought that 48 hours was not a very long time to take care of things if you also have to work, eat, and sleep. So before you knew it the by-law officer had glued a warning or a fine to your door. Our city has many cash cows. Snow removal, or the lack of it, is one of them.

While we were still fuming, a city crew would arrive and do the job. From the cab of a truck, three people would descend to take a look while the driver kept himself and the truck warm and cozy. The younger of the crew would start removing the snow from the sidewalk in an orderly fashion while the other two would discuss whatever members of a snow removal crew discuss in that situation. This is a ritual that can be observed in many cities all over the world where snow tends to fall. There must be an international union agreement dictating that for each working member of a city crew there must be at least two assessing the work done.

Now and then there is a coffee break, when they all huddle in the warm cab. The fee in tremendous. Do not talk to anyone in the first three hours after the poor soul has opened the envelope with the invoice. Avoid your spouse unless you are prepared for a divorce, bite your tongue and clamp your teeth together, try to think of the brighter side of life. If it snows in July, nature usually takes care of things.

This official snow removal business happened to old Bentley one winter when he had promised to look after his son's small farm for a couple of weeks and was unaware of the rough weather in the city. Old Bentley lived in a very modest house with more snow than most on the sidewalks because he had a corner lot. The air was blue and yellow around his abode for a week. Then there was this uncomfortable silence when one night the chinook, the mild wind from the mountains, melted most of the snow during its short visit. By morning it was again minus 20. But someone had taken advantage of the situation and adjusted the eaves on the house where the by-law officer lived so the melting snow quietly but surely dripped on his city-owned car parked in the driveway... By morning it was one solid iceberg on one solid sheet of ice. It would be impossible to move that car for the next couple of months. Even the by-law officer's own vehicle was not available, as the garage door was frozen solid as well, and refused to open.

The wagging tongues had it that old Bentley was the culprit, but there was no proof, no witnesses, no evidence. The same busy tongues reported that the by-law officer had to rent a car which the city declined to pay for as it claimed he already had a car and he could at least turn it in.

Part of that story is probably wishful thinking. The fact remains that the by-law officer moved to another part of the city and, more importantly, we found the handyman we had been looking for to fix the running toilet, the dripping faucet in the kitchen, and a whole lot more. Anybody who can manage to force a by-law officer to move by changing the direction of his eaves must have imagination, talent, patience, and good hands. Old Bentley even had a warm smile and he lived in the neighbourhood. He was probably much older than I, but he had no intention of giving in to old age. He worked for the neighbourhood for a long time, and I will always remember him with gratitude. He saved our house, our marriage, and he gave us peace of mind. He was there when we needed him. He was a blessing as we got older.

Now and then I think of the by-law officer, and my thoughts have mellowed. After all, he gave us Bentley, the handy handyman, and saved us from old age.

Chapter 7

I WILL LIVE UNTIL I DIE

Some people age so beautifully, almost disgustingly beautifully – and then there are those of us who just age. It is in the genes, they tell us, and there is not much a person can do but wait and watch. There does not seem to be any visible change from day to day. It is the same face in the mirror every morning. Sometimes the cheeks appear to be a little puffed, the eyes pinkish, and the hair looking very grey, but there is always an explanation: late night, sad movie, too good a book, hardly any sleep. All lame excuses. We are getting visibly older.

The trick is not to get seriously old.

My friend, Silver, rode off to higher hunting grounds some years ago. He was 96 and he was not old. He was a cowboy and he loved life, horses, good stories, and women – exactly in that order. He could spin a tale, and no matter how many times you heard it, you took pleasure in his performance. He would commence as soon as there was the smallest break in the conversation. You could count on Silver to fill a gap. The town was small and everyone knew everyone. I sometimes had the funny feeling that as Silver grew older, the gap was left on purpose.

One story he liked to act out was the one about two men who had a bet concerning the male population in another small town. One claimed that he could judge right away at first sight whether a man was married. They settled on a corner where two main streets met. The man was right about the first nine. The tenth was wrong. He was not a married man as the expert judged.

– But he looks like one. Does he not?

– Perhaps. But he is a bachelor.

– Then he just came out of the hospital.

– Right.

Silver would laugh, and his audience, big or small, would laugh with him.

Silver aged extremely well under circumstances that would have killed anyone else at a very early stage.

His castle was a one-room hut on the bald prairie where the horizon meets the sky in all four directions. Silver laboured in the open, training horses. He helped during harvest on the bigger farms and did not change underwear during the four weeks it lasted.

– What's the use? It gets dirty anyway.

No one complained, or came too close. They all worked in the open. His water supply was a slough where he had killed all life with a strong solution of chemicals that should have numbered his days as well. The water was cold and clear and dead, and there was enough of it because only Silver could stomach it. Even the coyotes refused it.

Silver did not acknowledge that the car had been invented. He had no use for it. He had his horse, named Silver.

– So I can remember her name, he laughed, and his laugh was good, warm, and genuine.

Every Saturday evening, the two Silvers left the hut on the prairie for a social, a get-together at the nearest beer parlour, some ten miles down the road. While one Silver went inside to lubricate his dried-up innards and tell stories, the other Silver waited faithfully outside until it was time for both to retreat. Silver Horse was always hitched in the same place so Silver Man had no trouble finding her, no matter how late, no matter what his status at that time. It was said that Silver Horse sometimes bent her knees in order for Silver Man to get on top of her.

One way or the other, Silver Man rode out of town often already asleep, and Silver Horse promenaded slowly homeward without any command or a hand to steer her. Once she reached the homestead, she bent her neck and started grazing, and Silver Man slid safely to the ground where he picked himself up the next morning. If it rained or if it was cold, Silver Horse would unload her master in the small grey unpainted barn where the door was always open.

Silver never grew old or admitted to old age. The words were not in his vocabulary. He did not own a mirror and had probably no idea how he looked. He shaved once a week, the day he went to town, and if he did not shave closely but left small clusters of hair, everyone knew he had made an effort, and that was good enough at the beer parlour. Silver Horse never noticed or expressed any concern. She trotted to town with her master, and carried him slowly and safely back, out of harm's way.

One day Silver Horse died in her sleep. Silver Man found her and he buried his friend exactly where she gave up. Some people said she was somewhere between thirty and forty years old. Silver Man dug a grave so deep that no wild animal could ever find and maul his beloved dead friend. It took him a week, and how he ever got that horse into that grave is anybody's guess. But he did. He then moved the soil back where it belonged, and Silver Horse was buried in an unmarked grave on the bald prairie.

Silver Man took a bath and changed his underwear, no one knows in what order. He went inside his hut and was never seen again.

One of his neighbours 15 miles down the road missed him because it was harvest time. The same neighbour also organized the burial by sending for a minister. Silver had not belonged to a church, so the neighbour just got hold of the nearest holy man.

– And a word or two can be said about his Silver Horse, the neighbour suggested. He had known Silver Man for thirty years without knowing anything about him.

– His horse... the minister frowned.

– His best friend, the horse. Yah.

– God is our best friend, corrected the minister.

The neighbour spread the word that no one should expect too much at that funeral, but the grub that followed would be good because all Silver's former girlfriends would bring food and drinks...

The minister, however, was not too bad at all. He talked about friendship between humans and animals, a little awkwardly, perhaps, but he did it – and he certainly enjoyed the wake.

– A lot of sisters that man had, he was heard muttering in between drinks – and so different from one another.

Silver never got old, not seriously old. His secret seemed to be that he lived, really lived, until the day he died.

Chapter 8

EAT YOUR GREEN VEGETABLES

Eat your green vegetables, do your exercise, smile, and you will be a happy senior. The older you get, the more you need these three ingredients in order to get older yet.

The trouble for us seniors is that the good people brimming over with advice and expertise have never been old themselves. It is unfortunately not a stage you can whip in and out of. Once there, you are caught. It is a life sentence. No prayers, no green vegetables, and no exercise can change that situation.

You can never say – last year when I was old... Last month when I was a senior...

You can say – last year when I was in Paris... Last month when I had my operation... Five years ago when I was younger...

To be a senior is not a passing sensation. It is simple and naked reality.

There is nothing to be scared of except the good intentions that force people to counsel you constantly. They even talk with a high-pitched voice that hurts your eardrums. It is as if you lost your common sense overnight and desire to be treated like a child – for your own sake.

But apart from that which can be corrected if you let them know that you do not wish for any special treatment just because you now are 65 years old, you become more and more aware of the pain in muscles and joints. The back gets sore, the neck is stiff, the feet are swollen, the energy is waning. Hopefully not everything at the same time. There is a depressed feeling that we will not get well again, that diseases have settled in to stay, and there is certainly the admission that there are many things we cannot do anymore or else they take forever to cope with.

Right. But that process did not start when we became seniors. It has been there for a long time, if we care to face facts. Unfortunately, it is brought to the foreground the second we cross the boundary between being a productive adult and a more or less helpless senior.

In self-preservation we have to forget the things we used to do with ease. Some of them can still be done with some management if we allow ourselves the time, some we have to give up, but in the big picture they are really not important or vital. It can be a matter of pride, but that is not worth the suffering. Let go of the impossible, the impractical, but heed your own counsel. We all have different ways of coping as the years go by, and one round big birthday nips at the next one. We all have our own recipes for getting old with grace.

No one is saying it is easy, but most people will admit that if you lose your sense of humour, you have lost your most salient weapon. If you can no longer enjoy the moment for fear of the future, find a rocking chair and stay there.

Life was really not so easy when we were younger. Remember when you lost your job or you did not get promoted. Junior was sick and the doctors could not find a cure for a long time. The car broke down and there was no money to fix it. Your youngest had to have her teeth corrected and there went the vacation you had dreamed about and saved for. The pain in your stomach, could that be cancer? The sleepless nights before the tests, and you were only 45.

– But I do not care what you say, something goes missing as we get older. The light in the tunnel is dimming.

Yes. Of course. We would not want to live until we are 200. We know we have to leave this earth one day, but we have known that all our lives as adults. No one promised us from the beginning that we would reach a ripe age. We could have keeled over years ago. So why stare at it now instead of enjoying the moments we have.

Richard was closing in on his 100th birthday, and the family had decided a big party was in order, with a picture in the paper and greetings from the heads of three governments. Richard had a hard time comprehending what all the fuss was about. He enjoyed his quiet life in the nursing home where they leave you alone most of the time. He sat in his wheelchair at the window and followed the sparrows fighting with each other. That is, if the birds came close to his windowsill. Otherwise he just sat buried in his own thoughts.

The commotion multiplied as the day grew closer. Family members who had not seen Richard for years were invited, neighbours who had forgotten him long ago promised to come and celebrate. The world should see he was still part of their lives. The youngest great-great-grandchild should sit on his wobbly knees when the photographer came. One could only hope she would not start to cry because she did not know the old man.

Richard got restless in the limelight. He liked his peace, his sleep in the wheelchair where nobody paid any attention. The night before the big event, it was decided to give him a bath, cut his hair and nails and thus let the world know he was well looked after.

Richard had no choice in the matter, and he was put to bed clean and well manicured. His best jacket was brushed and spots removed. The big cake was in the big fridge next to the kitchen. Richard – 100 years! it said in daring blue icing on a white background. Everything was ready. They came to his bed the next morning already singing "Happy birthday to you", and there was Richard, of course. He could not move without help. But Richard was dead. He died during the night.

– They will probably use the cake for his wake, smiled Richard's oldest son, who was 80 and had been against that birthday celebration from the beginning.

– Dad always got the last word, made the final decision.

When we were younger, big waves could carry us to the top of the world, perhaps only for a short while; other waves left us gasping for air, ready to crush us at the very bottom. We were in the mainstream, ready for battle, win or lose, prepared to take part in whatever life had to offer, pushing fate as much as we could. Sometimes we were exuberant, sometimes exhausted, but we never let go. Action was the name of the game.

Now we are anchored in a sheltered harbour. The waves are small and insignificant, they do not rock the boat. They can be irritating and produce sleepless nights. Our boats are getting old and fragile and would sink in stormy weather. We are supposed to be grateful and content in our sedate lifestyle.

– Take it easy, Dad. You have deserved your otium.

Yes, you have. But you have also the right to admit that something is missing. Some excitement, inspiration, emotion, even agitation. Everything is flat and almost colourless. There are no responsibilities, no obligations – we are really not needed anymore! That makes you feel empty and old. So do not believe it, do something about it.

But what to do when the whole world has already decided for us?

– Just enjoy life, Mom. Play bridge, make new friends.

That really means – Sit in your soft chair in front of your television and watch time go by. Count the hours until you swallow your sleeping pills and drown you depression for a while.

– You are lucky, Dad. You do not have to battle the morning traffic anymore.

We do not have to battle anything!

Sometimes when we were younger and life crashed right over our heads, we wished for a few peaceful days with no worries, no people to disturb us. But we never wanted it day after day, week after week, an endless continuation of nothing, a bare existence without emotions and happenings.

In our disgust, we start complaining about trivial details we never paid attention to before. We become old grumps, petty-minded, critical and negative.

– It happens to older people all the time. They do not have a worry in the world, and yet they are thankless and dissatisfied.

No, absolutely not. We are not thankless and we are not dissatisfied, but we are going through a change that hurts. As teens we went through a transition stage, and that was not easy, but it was accepted and partly understood, mostly by our friends, who suffered as we did. Even our parents tried to comprehend what was going on because they were young and vaguely remembered they had felt the same, but mostly because they knew us and loved us. They wanted the best for us.

They were confronted with our moods every day.

– Betty, what is the matter? Talk to me. I am your mother. I will try to understand. Why is everything all of a sudden so wrong? You used to be such a happy child.

– But Mom, I am not a child anymore.

– I know you are growing up. Heavens above, I am keenly aware of what is going on, after all I was a teenager myself once.

A little laugh, a half-smile, the beginning of a bridge where understanding can travel back and forth.

That was then. Now you are an older person, supposed to be wise and experienced, and you have to journey on your own without knowing the reason for your discontent. Life is hard to deal with. This business of getting older is not what you thought it would be. Why can't body, soul, and mind age at the same tempo?

Do we expect too much, or do we not have the wisdom and the courage to face what is going on within ourselves? Does the body want what the mind will not give it, or is the mind demanding too much? Is the soul taking over, leaving the body and the mind on their own?

– I do not understand...

How can you, when you do not even try?

– I know I am not seventeen anymore.

My dear, it is a long time ago that you were seventeen. You are seventy or more. Face it and live with it. But you are really not old. Not today.

As Elvira said when I was driving her to the beauty parlour – I thought I was old and finished when I was 70, and now I am 98. How dumb I was. I almost stopped living. I wasted a lot of good time.

There are no remedies to make time stand still, and all the green vegetables in the world cannot change the fact that we are getting older. There were days where we pined for tranquility, and now that we have it we grump and growl and feel left out.

That is were we are wrong. We are needed and wanted in so many places if we make an effort to find out where experience and age are considered assets. Time is ours, so we have to use it satisfactorily, or it will be a burden, often too heavy to carry. Granted there are tasks we cannot cope with anymore – leave them alone and delight in what is still possible. That is how Wilma gets through her days...

– I praise myself for the things I manage to do and forget about the rest.

Deep in our hearts we all know how we would like to occupy ourselves. The choice is ours, and as long as we have a choice, life can be very challenging, interesting, and exciting, regardless of age. Let no one decide what you ought to do. You know best, so go ahead and do it. Just because we are seniors, we are not sheep, ready to follow whoever leads. We are individuals, slowed down a little by arthritis or some other disabilities. We sometimes act a little silly. That is also our choice. We can still love and laugh and enjoy life. We still have a lot to give. We will not let anyone tell us how to use our time.

We can eat our green vegetables. If we want to. As long as we remember they are not the solution to our problems as we grow older.

Though old as the hills

If you count my years

My heart still harbours

A youthful laughter

Because I can taste

The sweetness of life

Chapter 9

MEMORIES ARE MADE OF...

It is not such a good idea, but we do it anyway. One day, without any thought of the consequences, we find the old albums with all the old pictures of all the young people, ourselves when we were young, and younger, and very young. They are stowed away behind some useless junk that once seemed to be valuable enough to buy.

Great Scot, was I really that slim and fit... and that young! Look at me now, with my broad behind, the wrinkled face, and the double chin.

Here we are in Rome, looking a little lost because we were lost. But did we care? No. We just marched on knowing only three Italian words, and we did find our hotel four hours later. We even met some other tourists who had lost their way.

– Follow us, we said, brimming over with youthful confidence.

– Are you sure you know where you are going, the other people asked.

No. We were absolutely not sure. We just pretended. What could we lose? We had already lost our way. The other couple thanked us profusely when we finally found the hotel. I wish they had taken the picture then.

But they called us – our perfect guides. You certainly know Rome like your own pocket.

Tired and dusty, we settled down to a cappuccino. A little later I heard the wife whisper to her husband – How come it took us twenty minutes to get there and four hours to walk home?

He just smiled. – Rome was not built in a day, he whispered, and she smiled back. They were young, too, and in love, as we were. And here is the picture to remind me.

There was another time in Rome, many years later. It was a conference of a sort, and we kept to a short radius around the hotel. We were older and had lost the carefree approach to life. We could get lost!

Of course we never did. How can you if you do not venture out? We met the same shops and the same restaurants every day. The only memento from that trip is a group picture. Two hundred important people. We are in the seventh row. As you get older there is safety in numbers.

There are pictures from the time we built the summer cottage. We were working hard, grinning, happy and dirty, into the sun. Did we really build that cottage ourselves? Yes, we did. From the ground up: two bedrooms and a nice combined kitchen-, dining-, and living room. We went fishing an hour before lunch, and had always enough to eat. We dined on pickerel and perch with potatoes roasted over open fire. The children were children then. They followed us wherever we went without judging our decisions.

It was later, only a few years later, they started doubting our abilities.

– Are you sure, Mum? Because Helen's dad said...

Helen's dad must have been a pro. He always knew what to do, and did the right thing at the right moment.

– It will pass, we assured each other. – We were good enough before.

I do not know if it passed. It rather changed to a patient admission that most parents are old fashioned and very often do not have a clue what is going on in this world. Even Helen's dad was known to have made mistakes, according to Helen.

There are pictures of children and birthday cakes with candles, smiling children ready to blow, and get a year older by doing so. I can hear our dad's appealing – Say cheese. We all said cheese and looked that way.

Another page in the album and a youngster in a dark gown and mortarboard. A happy day filled with worries for the future and how to pay the bills. Still, a good day to be a parent. A proud day.

– She needs further education. One degree is not enough today. No vacation this year or next. No complaints. One day, dear, we will discover the world together... One day.

Suddenly there is a beautiful young lady in a long white dress with laces and a huge bouquet of flowers. A wedding. The next generation promising to love and cherish each other. We parents are the supporting staff.

– You are so young. He is so young...

– Mum, what were you doing at my age…?

Silence and a meek – Expecting you, dear.

That was during the weeks leading up to the pictures of the happy couple and their parents. Did we ever try to look worry-free.

We were wrong again. Thirty years later, the young couple still walk hand in hand, followed by two young men who once were babies. The grandchildren.

– Cheers. All the best. To your future.

The young people smile. So sure of themselves. There is nothing they cannot tackle. Recognize the smile. It once was yours.

Well, will you look at that picture. You are in a silver dress. You have been married 25 years, and the groom makes a speech at the big family dinner.

– It has been an interesting journey. Thank you, my dearest, for all the memories…

Some of them you could have lived without, but the sad ones disappear in the fog that silvery night.

– Without you, I would never have made it…, he continues.

– At least, not the children – Lenny, a friend of the family, suggests. He is the court joker

A glorious night never to be forgotten.

More pictures from the cottage. The children are somewhere else because they are no longer children, so we take turns with the camera.

– Here is your dad emptying the biffy...

– Here is your mom, all wet because she insisted on taking the boat out alone. Yes, somebody towed her home.

Why did I insist on taking the boat out alone? The time would come soon enough where I had to do everything alone.

The trees we planted have grown. The cottage needs painting. The biffy does not have to be emptied that often.

– Congratulations... You are grandparents. The voice over the phone is jubilant... It is long-distance. Very long-distance.

– A little girl...

Grandmother and Grandfather. Big huge words with a lot of responsibilities. You promise yourself that you are not going to be one of those ever-bragging, irritating grandparents who thinks the world turns around the youngest addition and everyone adores her first smile, her first tooth, and her first word that sounds like Gram.

But there you are, the first time you meet your friends.

– You would not believe it, but my granddaughter... Your friends seem to avoid you for a while.

Not to worry. It comes with the title. All grandparents do it.

They come visiting, the young couple and the granddaughter. The little one is playing with her feet on the carpet, three times vacuum-cleaned.

– Please take your shoes off, Emmeline. The knitting bee is invited to watch the wonder from a safe distance.

– But you never wanted us to take our shoes off. You always said that one is supposed to walk on the floors.

– My granddaughter is on the floor. Your shoes, please, Emmeline...

There is no room for arguments or suggestions or negotiations. They all sit around in stocking feet and watch the wonder on the floor yet too young to move.

– Look at her...

As if they dared to do anything but...

By the time the little one is walking from room to room, like a hurricane destroying objects in her wake, her little brother is safely secured in a playpen out of harm's way. You are really supposed to walk on floors.

Lots and lots of pictures. Some good, some should have been thrown away long ago. You are glad no one bothered. They all remind you, and it is a good feeling to remember, even if it hurts, or because it hurts. Everybody is growing up and growing older. The original group is getting smaller. You meet at wakes to celebrate a life that stopped and is no longer.

– We are here to remember Ernestine...

Oh no. Not Ernestine. You can still hear her laughter. But you will not hear it again. She was such a good friend, always ready to help and to forgive.

– Remember when we were in the mountains, riding, and Ernestine got a horse that refused to move. She said she had a wonderful time with the horse. She also once invited us all for tea and her dog ate the sandwiches while she was at the door letting us in...

Once we forgot her... Where was that...? It was raining that day... Oh, I have forgotten where it was...

She was always so positive although she did not have an easy life. It is hard to celebrate when your heart is crying. Another friend gone.

The wakes seem like pearls on a string. Once, we were so many; but now... And they all look frail and much older, including yourself.

Once the whole bunch went camping together, husbands and wives and children and dogs and cats. It was fun and laughter. We were constantly cooking or doing dishes or searching for a stray child or a cat or a dog. One night a wife disappeared. It was Carlos Demorando's better half. He was not really concerned.

– Who will steal Liza, I ask you? He had a heavy Greek accent. His beard was black and he had manly hair on a manly chest. – They will bring her back when they see her in daylight.

Carlos went back to sleep. We knew his snoring by then. But we were worried and fanned out in small shivering parties. Where could Liza be? The moon was out, the shadows were scary. We called her name again and again. No one answered.

– She must have taken a leak and never found her way back, Louis suggested in his soft English with a French accent. He did not mind the walk in the warm moonlit summer night. His tent was over-crowded with three children, one cat, two dogs, and his wife. Louis found it was a nice intermission, and he knew that Ian had a bottle. Ian went nowhere without a bottle. No man with respect for himself did that in Ireland, where he came from.

We finally got a campfire going. Ian was not the only one with a bottle. Everyone came prepared. Ian started singing. It got quite loud and colourful. We all joined. You could hardly hear the snoring from Carlos' tent. It was happy hour until a sharp voice in no uncertain terms commanded us to shut up.

Dead silence. The voice belonged to Liza, but it came from the wrong tent.

– Good night! Ian managed to say. – What is she doing in our tent?

– You have a party and I am not invited. Liza came out from a tent, all cold cream and curlers.

She must have been out on her nightly business and wandered into the wrong tent.

– I never noticed, Ian said.

– You wouldn't, said his wife.

It was time to douse the fire and go back to sleep, but now the children were awake and demanded breakfast, and the dogs started howling. It was all sorted out somehow. The camp was a huge success.

Next week the menfolk took off on their own. They needed a rest, they insisted.

There were other camps, and we enjoyed them all. Sometimes it poured from the moment we left our quiet street in the city until we returned. The campground was noisy and overcrowded. We had forgotten the meat and all the plates. The rain stopped Monday morning. But we had already plans for the next and the next weekend. We all had sore backs and there was a mountain of washing to do. The old wringer washing machine tried, sometimes in vain, to cope with the huge loads. But we had fun and we were all there.

Once we talked about a reunion. It never came off.

– Did we really go camping in a tent...? the children who are no longer children ask with doubt in their eyes. – And it was fun?

Yes it was. And we have the memories, those of us who can still remember the happy days. We can recall incidences and happenings. We feel the warmth in our hearts, and a smile is ready on our lips. We are older now. We are not that old. We do have the memories.

Though old as the hills

If you count my years

My heart still harbours

A youthful laughter

Because I can taste

The sweetness of life

Chapter 10

TO DO – OR NOT

It is an established opinion, especially among the younger generation, that we older people ought to learn something, as if we have not done it before.

– Take a course, Dad... ...Go to a class, Mom.

The suggestions are plentiful.

– You have time now. Nothing else to do...

Some parents are very easily convinced, or they just do it to be left alone. My friend Emmeline and I do not belong to that group. We are stubborn and obstinate, our children claim, and just because the thought is not our own idea we dismiss it right away.

– Mom has always been like that.

A little shamefully, I have to admit they are very close to the truth.

Emmeline defended herself by saying she has learned enough to last her a lifetime. I do not have that excuse. I just remember that school days were not as happy as they could have been. That can happen very easily when you are number six of seven children and the teachers still remember with glee the older part of the family.

– How come your older sister is so intelligent, the teacher would wonder out loud, and stare at me in disbelief. – So beautiful, and so pleasant.

For a long time I thought that each family had a certain portion of intelligence and beauty to share, and the older siblings did not leave very much to the younger ones.

Emmeline and I held the fort through three winters.

Then the pressure was too much and we gave in.

The big question was what to learn.

– No cooking lessons, Emmeline said.

– No one in my house wants to eat that fancy stuff they teach.

I agreed. After all, we have kept our families alive for many years with good old-fashioned stand-bys, so why change our style now?

Agreement. Unanimous consent.

– Let us be positive, Emmeline suggested after we had discarded all ideas for two hours. We settled on a language. You can never know too many languages. The world is full of them.

– Spanish, Emmeline said. Her secret dream has been to go to Spain and dance with a Spanish toreador who does not believe in bullfighting but would rather trip around with Emmeline in his strong arms. She mentioned it every time we saw Carmen. Now was the moment to do something about it.

The thought of tight-stepping with a Spanish bullfighter was really not my idea of happiness. My desire went more to Venice and a soft-singing gondolier who only had eyes for me because I was the only passenger in his gondola...

Emmeline was, however, adamant, and deep in my heart, I had to admit that it was a little late in life to be dreaming about romancing in Venice. Furthermore, I could not care less which language we learned. I would, under all circumstances, rather sit at home and watch Law and Order...

– Do your want to face the children once more without having decided? Emmeline chimed in, and she was right.

– Spanish, she repeated, with a dangerous glint in her blue eyes.

Spanish it was. We sent for brochures, and the mailman had a busy time.

Talk Spanish in two weeks. Understand Spanish within a week. Learn Spanish and be happy. And there were pictures of people who laughed and seemed to be having a wonderful time. Perhaps this Spanish business was not such a dumb idea.

Emmeline said she was sure our teacher would be tall, slender around the hips, sexy and elegant. He would of course have broad shoulders and white teeth. Emmeline said that is how the Spaniards are.

We had selected to go to the community hall for our lessons. They happened to have ballroom dancing in the adjacent room and ice hockey outside. Both classes worked with blaring, although different, music.

– I am sure we will pay no attention to that when our class starts. Emmeline spoke with energetic persuasion. I was only half convinced. I nodded and smiled. A long life has taught me, among other things, to make the best of a situation. When there is no way out.

– Let us hope so.

Emmeline smiled back. It was worth the effort.

Our teacher turned out to be a little overweight, a fraction undersized, with thin hair and round shoulders. I would have taken him for a Canadian any day. I am sure he was. There was nothing wrong with his teeth, and he did have a nice smile. We had to settle for two out of ten.

He knew his Spanish. Not that I am an authority on the subject, but it sounded good, and his hands flew through the air and cut it into small pieces. Our class was a solid mixture of mature people who had been convinced they had to take a course and had refused to enroll in a cooking class.

There was a lot of yawning, and the chair felt like rock after ten minutes. Sometimes it was really hard to hear what our teacher tried to teach us because of the music from the ballroom dancing and the noise from the ice rink. The hearing aids seemed to pick it all up without discretion. It was a queer mixture, indeed.

However, most of the first lesson was conducted in English, and that we understood. Our Spanish toreador had no accent at all. We discussed mostly which books we should use and if there was a dictionary available for under ten dollars.

Unfortunately all Spanish dictionaries were sold out. Emmeline and I used a lot of time looking in all the local bookstores.

– No one learns Spanish nowadays, a young clerk confided to me. She was pretty close.

The books were out of print and had been for several years. One bookstore offered us an English-German dictionary on sale for 7 dollars.

– Spanish, German. They are both foreign languages, he said. His sales pitch impressed us as being a little odd.

It turned out one elderly gentleman had bought an English-English dictionary, whatever that is. He claimed he could not afford a Spanish dictionary even if it were available. He was on fixed income and his rent had been increased. He held us imprisoned with his life-story for more than twenty minutes. He had been in the navy in his young days, and he used a few juicy English words I had never heard before. The evening was not completely wasted.

– Perhaps we should have enrolled in an English class, I mumbled, certain that Emmeline would detect my sarcasm. But she was absolutely hypnotized by the elderly gentleman's story.

– I think he was on the same ship as my Harry, she whispered – I mean during the war.

So we both got something out of the class.

The teacher had brought his thermos and a sandwich, which he enjoyed while the former sailor had the floor.

– Let me look into the book situation, he promised, while inviting waltz music drifted in from the ballroom class, mixed with the yapping from the ice arena. It was all very interesting. Our teacher suggested everyone should bring something to eat and drink next time, which we did. Let it not be said we had given up food because of Spanish.

Potluck is always a challenge. My friends are Greek, Italian, French, Swedish, and Danish. I had no idea what to cook so it could be called Spanish Delight.

I phoned the teacher at home. He would steer me in the right direction.

That was a mistake of major proportions. His mother answered the phone. She was not a Spanish delight.

– You know my son? Her voice was suspicious.

– Oh yes, I answered truthfully, without realizing the consequences.

– You are not Spanish, she hissed, and I felt that remark was not in my favour.

– Nono, no. Heaven forbid. I laughed. I should not have laughed...

If you are a female, you do not laugh when you are talking to a suspicious, mistrusting Spanish mother.

– You know my son very well? Her voice grew very hostile. – And he gave his phone number?

– Not exactly, I had to admit. It had taken an hour to trace it.

– Just what I thought. Her voice was menacing now. – He is not home...

Perhaps I could leave a message.

– Whatever for...?

– So he could call me back, I suggested.

– My son, he never calls no dame...

Our conversation was interrupted when she slammed the receiver down and gave me no chance to explain that I was a harmless senior who had grabbed onto Spanish lessons as a last resort. I was not interested in her son; I still had good eyes, with my bifocals on. She did not give me an opportunity to soothe her anxiety.

She got me rather upset with her rudeness, and in my anger I decided to make Danish meatballs because I like them and right then I could not care less what they ate in Spain.

The next class was rather interesting. The ballroom people were learning the rumba. The whole community center was shaking. Our local ice hockey team had invited their arch-rivals to play for reasons unknown, which accounted for the excessive yelling and screaming from the arena. Again I heard words I had to learn. Our teacher brought Spanish books, but not enough to go around. Emmeline moved over to the sailor right away. She later discovered he was legally blind. But that evening she blossomed in his compliments.

– He said to me... Are you really a senior? Emmeline blushed with pride and happiness.

Her desertion left me with a former pound employee who smelled as if he still worked, although he disclosed he had been retired for almost ten years.

The food was amazing. Everyone had given up on Spanish Delight and brought paper napkins and plastic forks. One person placed a flag from Portugal on the table. There were 12 of us, and we had to share 18 Danish meatballs. The navy man fortunately had a bottle of something strong and illegal. The navy always comes prepared for dangerous situations.

The teacher ate his own Spanish Delight and never offered to share. He mentioned that some idiot had phoned his mother.

I nearly blushed.

The next lesson was conducted in Spanish and I have no idea what went on. It sounded foreign and strange, and the teacher's movements were almost obscene. His mother should have seen him now! Apparently it was a lesson in how you boarded a bus in Madrid, and that apparently was how they did it. If I ever land in Madrid – by mistake, mind you – I will stay at the airport and look for the next flight out. I will never be able to get on a bus. Even Emmeline on the way home had to admit that Spanish busses were not for her.

Fewer and fewer students came to the classes. It happens all the time.

At the weekly knitting bee, one member told us about a cooking class she was taking.

– And you should see the teacher! Her eyes sought the ceiling and she smacked her lips as she described an Italian gondolier... After that, even Emmeline gave up.

– I wanted to learn to speak the language, was her defense – not go on a bus.

She had a point...

My family is known for its stubbornness. I had paid good money against my better judgement to learn Spanish, and Spanish I would learn. I continued without Emmeline. There are a few things in life I have done without Emmeline. Not many, but some.

The ballroom dancing had finished and the ice was melting. There was peace in our community hall, and that night I was the only student present. That night my teacher had also forgotten his thermos and his sandwich at home, so his mother arrived at half time with both in her motherly arms, only to find her beloved son alone in the building with a lady, so to speak.

– Buenas tardes, señora, I said, with a feeling that it was payback time.

She stood still for a moment.

– I thought you had better taste. She turned around and left, with her son's Spanish Delight and thermos. He knew better that to try to apprehend her.

It is fall again, and the children are after their old parents.

– Take a course, Dad. Go to a class, Mom.

– Not until I have seen a picture of the teacher, Emmeline told her tribe.

Mine is goading me.

– Perhaps Mom is too old now for that.

It took a long night's thinking before I unveiled my plans for the coming winter.

– I have decided to learn to fly. I always wanted to look at everything from above.

There was a family meeting shortly after that announcement, I understand. One of the girls said – Perhaps we are pushing Mum too hard. Perhaps we should leave her alone.

That would not be such a bad idea.

Give us seniors a helping hand when needed, but do not try to take over. We know how to live our own lives. We actually enjoy living.

Chapter 11

OLD AGE CAN WAIT

There are different ways to combat old age.

Maxine had a pattern she followed for a long time with success.

When she opened her eyes in the morning, ready to face a new day, she would fetch the newspaper, put on her trifocals, and read it.

She would study it carefully and slowly because she wanted to know how the world had behaved while she was having her beauty rest. Last item was the page with the obituaries. That is not so uncommon for the older population, we just hope we will not find a familiar name, but sometimes it is sad reading.

However, Maxine's intent was different. She looked for her own name. Her pinky would move from ad to ad, and if she did not find it, she would conclude that she was still among the living and it was time for strong coffee, toast, jam and cheese. She enjoyed it all with an exuberant feeling of relief.

One morning, however, when she was reading that black-framed page, she stopped cold, and very disturbed, because here was her full name, correctly spelled, to inform the world that she had passed away peacefully two days ago.

That made Maxine very sad, of course, and she stayed in bed with the newspaper pressed to her heart. What was the use of drinking strong coffee with toast, jam, and cheese if you had already passed away?

After a while, still in her bed, Maxine felt a strange sensation. She recognized the hunger pangs and wondered why she had not eaten her breakfast. She slowly rose from the dead and made her way out to the kitchen, where she took care of things. But that was the day she decided that no one was going to tell her she was getting old, let alone dead. She ignored the paper until she had done her exercise, had a shower and some juice, and on good mornings even a walk around the block.

– It is up to ourselves, was her war cry. – We are not old until we feel that way.

Every time Maxine tells that story she adds a little colour and a few extra words. Once she finishes, you feel like applauding a good actress.

My discovery of the advancing grey years was much more down to earth, but then my whole life has been that way compared to Maxine's. I lack the ability to colour and expand the events.

My mother told me to be truthful, no matter what. That advice has often put me in serious trouble and awkward situations. My few friends and my family know that what I say is the whole truth and nothing but the truth, and they cringe every time I start recalling a situation or an event with all the details, good and bad.

I tried to instill the same moral in my own children, but luckily enough they were more critical of their mother's wisdom and intelligence. Two of them even became lawyers. Their doubt seems to have made life a little easier for all of them.

Back to my day of discovery.

It was a fine morning with sunshine and a whisper of spring in the air. The city streets had been washed clean by an April shower. It was one of the days where you have to get out of the house and do something, which

I did, and found myself waiting for an elevator in a four-story department store.

Elevators arrive immediately if you have lots of time, but if you are in a hurry, it gets stuck between two floors or will not move from the third level because somebody just met somebody and keeps the door open in order to hear the latest.

That day the elevator arrived with no hesitation and the door flung open. At that very moment a young mother with a cute little girl headed for the lift. The cute little girl was in a hurry because that is how little girls behave when they see an elevator.

The mother tried to hold her back and said – Elsie, darling. You have to learn to let old people in first. It is bad manners to push ahead of an elderly lady.

I was brought up very well too, so I moved away from the open door to let the old lady in first.

Surprise! There was nobody there but myself.

– Go ahead, smiled the mother to me.

A chilling dreadful thought filled my stomach, if thoughts can do that. I was the old lady they were talking about. Impossible. I was a middle-aged lady with spring feelings in my heart.

I straightened my back and squared my shoulders and said – I think I will walk up to the fourth floor. It is good for you to use the stairs. Just to show them that is what old ladies do around here.

Have you ever walked up four floors in a department store? The stairs are not meant for going up – only down. It is like 8 flights in an ordinary building. After all, that is why they have the elevators.

I was more than half dead when I finally reached the fourth floor, sweaty, hot, and uncomfortable, red in the face, and my feet were killing me. I leaned towards a wall, hoping I would survive, when who do you think came towards me down the aisle? You are right, the motherly mother and her cute little girl, both looking fresh and content, their business completed.

Children are so observant. That is the way they learn in life. What do you think the little girl said when she saw me hanging on to the wall?

She yelled with that clear piercing voice that belongs to little girls – Look, Mom, there is the old lady again!

This time I was almost convinced.

Of course we get older every day. No sense in denying. The question is: when are we initiated into the ranks of old age?

We are individuals, and old age does not strike at a certain moment on a certain day. It tends to creep up on us, slowly but surely – sooner if we allow it.

There is no doubt that health plays a big role. Sick people are often not able to fight back, although there are seniors riddled with serious diseases, and they still have that special optimistic outlook on life. They simply do not think of themselves as old; they carry their burden with dignity, patience, and a bright smile. They are the people who have decided to live every day, be it ever so close to the edge.

They often have to count every penny, and an unexpected expense can push them over the brink, financially. They still face each morning with optimism. They are young at heart and they believe God gave no human being a burden he or she cannot carry. They are old, yes, and they sometimes look a little decrepit. An older person is like an older house: Upkeep is important, and upkeep costs money. When their comrades in arms visit a beauty parlour every week, the poorer seniors will attack their thin hair with a pair of dull scissors. The result can be rather amazing and look like a lawn mowed with a hedge-trimmer. Fortunately their eyes are often too weak to take in the result. It certainly does not defuse their life spirit... Their clothes are often from a second-hand store. One shirt, 25 cents. One blouse, 35 cents. It is perhaps the wrong colour and not exactly the right size. But it is a shirt or a blouse, so who cares? It is washed in the kitchen sink and dried in the tiny bathroom where its wet corners touch your head when you sit on the throne. They do not complain.

– I have a roof over my head and a bed where I can sleep, said Louise with her special smile. She is 89 and needs new glasses. She is on a waiting list for dentures. She has been for quite some time.

– Perhaps other people need dentures more than I do.

Louise refuses to accept that she landed on a big shelf reserved for very old people who are supposed to fade away in peace. They have lived too long already.

I happened to be there when she died. Her face was peaceful, her mouth, closed. You could not see her rotten teeth or imagine the pain they must have given her over the years. She was old, yes, but she did not give up on life until the moment she died. She had not reached old age in her mind. She was 89 and still on the waiting list to have her teeth fixed.

There were three of us at the funeral. A minister friend of mine, myself, and a very young paperboy who happened to pass the graveyard.

Louise was an angel on earth, but why did she have to be on a waiting list all that time? Life is not a dress rehearsal. Life is all there is.

We still had to clear Louise's tiny apartment: one room with an electric hotplate and a sink, the tiny bathroom where her blouse used to dry. A second-hand store owner had promised to come around...

He had dirty fingernails and demanded 50 dollars to remove Louise's belongings.

– It is junk, he said, and spat on the floor.

Louise had left 81 cents in a chipped cup. That should have carried her through the rest of the month.

The situation became unfriendly.

– This is not junk. This was the home of a very dear lady, and you can go to hell – I pointed to the door.

He disappeared without a word, but with some anxiety in his cunning eyes. Perhaps he thought I had been let out of an institution too early. They do that nowadays.

Louise would have said I was silly, because things meant nothing to her, but I carried each and every one of her belongings down the stairs myself, box after box, and the young paperboy helped with the bed. We hauled it with as much dignity as you can get from a rented truck to a place where young mothers pick up things they need free of charge. That part Louise would have loved. She was satisfied with a roof over her head and a bed to rest her weary legs. I still have her chipped cup with the 81 cents – and a letter that confirms her waiting is over. She has been accepted as a patient so her teeth can be looked after. It came three weeks after we buried her. She died young at heart. Old age never touched her.

It is different with Ernie, an educated man who has travelled the world and now views it from his wheelchair in a bright living room while his daily help looks after his needs. He is a philosopher and loves an audience.

– Old age is an attitude, he argues. – If you decide you are old, you have entered old age. Until then you are just an age-advanced senior.

We make our mistakes and we live with the consequences as we always have done.

Let no one push us into old age as long as we enjoy life.

Let us live until we die.

Though old as the hills
If you count my years
My heart still harbours
A youthful laughter
Because I can taste
The sweetness of life